D0457837

The
TRAVELER
and the
HEAVY
BURDEN

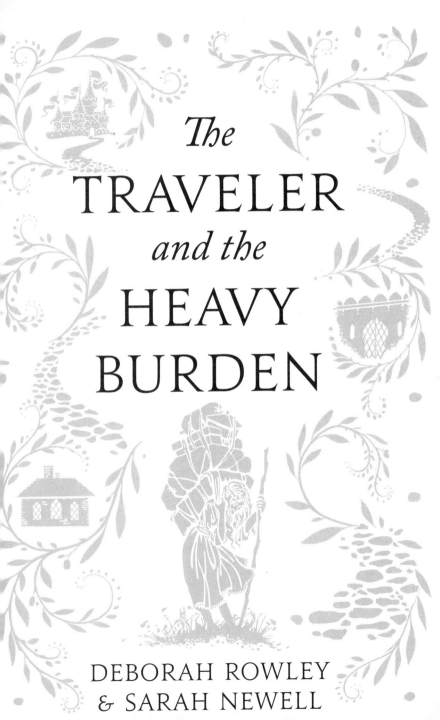

The
TRAVELER
and the
HEAVY
BURDEN

DEBORAH ROWLEY
& SARAH NEWELL

Published by Covenant Communications, Inc.
American Fork, Utah

Printed in the United States of America
First Printing: October 2019

25 24 23 22 21 20 19   10 9 8 7 6 5 4 3 2

ISBN: 978-1-52441-158-9

TO ALL MY FELLOW TRAVELERS

—Deborah Rowley

DEDICATED TO MY FAMILY, WITHOUT
WHOSE CONTINUAL LOVE AND SUPPORT, I
WOULD NOT BE THE PERSON I AM TODAY

—Sarah Newell

Come unto me, all ye that labour and are heavy laden, and I will give you rest. Take my yoke upon you, and learn of me; for I am meek and lowly in heart: and ye shall find rest unto your souls. For my yoke is easy, and my burden is light.

MATTHEW 11:28–30

THE ROAD

ONCE, THERE WAS A ROAD running like a ribbon through the world. Beautiful ladies in carriages raced past, followed by handsome men on horses. Farmers in wagons and merchants on donkeys shouted greetings to each other. Walking more slowly than everyone else, a traveler pushed on in the dust, carrying an enormous pack on her back.

The pack was overflowing with boxes and burdens tied into a towering pile held precariously in place with thick, knotted rope. This unusual tower cast its own deep shadow in the dirt and made the traveler shiver in the shade that she seemed to carry everywhere she went. The pack hid her face from those who passed her by. Perhaps that was the reason no one slowed to offer assistance but instead threw out judgments that added to the weight of her load.

Hour after hour, the traveler trudged on. Sunny moments turned to cloudy days, which became dreary weeks and darker months without respite from her inner storm. The road stretched unchanging before her as far as the eye could see until her desires diminished to one desperate wish: she wanted to be done.

That was it.

She thought she had cared about other things in the past, but now all she wanted was for the journey to be over.

She didn't know how she could take another step.

That was when the miracles began.

THE INN

THE FIRST MIRACLE OCCURRED WHEN the traveler reached a small inn at the side of the road. She didn't go in, just stepped off the path and sat heavily on the bench near the door. She wasn't seeking shelter because the pack prevented her from going inside. Long ago, she had quit trying to remove the pack, for she knew it couldn't be done.

Just then, the innkeeper leaned out a window and looked down. Without a word, he carried a steaming bowl of soup and a warm piece of bread through the doorway of the inn and handed them to the woman.

She ate hungrily while the innkeeper busied himself with something above her. She couldn't see what he was doing, for the pack prevented her from lifting her head.

When she finished eating and fumbled for a coin, the innkeeper bent down and looked kindly into her eyes. "Please see our king. I know he can help you. Do not travel onward without requesting an audience at the castle. Promise me you will."

"I promise," the traveler mumbled as she rose with her pack and slowly lumbered away.

The innkeeper watched the traveler until her shadow disappeared in the distance. Only then did he look sadly at the knife in his hands and the frayed rope at his feet. He bent to retrieve the heavy box he had quietly removed from the top of the traveler's pile and placed on the stairs while she was eating. *Helpless* it read in harsh, angry script. She hadn't yet noticed that it was gone.

THE GATE

ACK ON THE ROAD, THE traveler wished she could forget the innkeeper's words, but they kept repeating themselves in her mind. Was it possible? Could it be true? Of course she didn't believe him, but almost in spite of herself, she turned toward the king's city. By the time her feet had carried her to the imposing city wall, it was dark. *It is too late*, she thought. No one wants to be bothered at this hour. So she turned off the path into the woods surrounding the city, and there she collapsed against a large tree, rested her head on the hard lumps of the pack, and began to cry. Eventually, she drifted off to sleep.

She must have slept deeply, because by the time she awoke, dozens of people lined the road into the king's city. The traveler struggled to stand and then moved out of the trees to join them. To her dismay, as she reached the entrance, her tall pack caught in the archway and refused to budge, jamming the way into the city. She tugged at it hopelessly.

"Can't someone please help me?" she cried.

Guards pulled from the front, and the crowd shoved from behind but without success.

Suddenly, the mob behind her parted and grew still. The traveler felt hands tug at her pack. Miraculously, one of the heavy ropes fell at her feet, and a box was lifted from the enormous pile and set aside. *Hopeless* it read in bright-red letters stamped repeatedly on the box—*hopeless*.

Then an older woman spoke softly in her ear. "Do not feel trapped. Your life can change. I have been where you are, and the change happened for me. I promise you there is hope."

She tried to look back at her benefactor, but the crowd rushed forward, pushing her into the city. When she turned around, whoever had helped her was gone.

THE MARKET

In a daze, the traveler began to search for the castle. She couldn't lift her head high enough to see its glistening spires above the thatched roofs of the other buildings. She couldn't ask for directions for fear of what others might say. But somehow, she knew she needed to reach the highest point in the city; she felt that was where she would find the king's palace.

With one halting step after another, she climbed the steep cobblestone streets. "I can do this. I can do this," she repeated to herself. Perhaps yesterday it would have been impossible, but today she carried fewer burdens.

As she searched, there were dead ends and wrong turns that led down blind alleys and to locked gates, but the traveler kept moving.

Finally, she reached an open courtyard.

There, courtiers lingered over stalls at a royal bazaar. As the traveler reached the square, the hustle and bustle of business stopped, and people began to whisper and point at the pack. The traveler slinked back into the shadows, but she didn't see the peddler of silk scarves until she bumped hard against him.

The man turned in anger and pushed her out of his way. "Get away from here, ugly mule. You're scaring away business."

The traveler stumbled and fell on her hands in a pile of dung behind the scarf peddler's horse. The man

sneered in disgust. "Now you smell as bad as you look."

At that moment, someone's feet appeared beside the traveler, and a young woman whispered, "Do not listen, lady. You are beautiful and worth more than all the goods in this marketplace. The peddler doesn't know. You are more than your appearance, more than your condition—so much more."

The traveler again felt hands tugging at the pack on her back as another rope dropped limply to the ground.

The young woman lifted another heavy burden and set it aside.

The traveler looked at the painful letters carved into the box: *Worthless*.

The kind stranger placed several scarves she had purchased on top of the box to cover the word. Then she handed the traveler a few more scarves, damp from the fountain, to wash her hands.

After a moment, the traveler stood more easily and peered around the remaining burdens to see who had come to her aid. But she was alone. "Thank you," she said to the scarves in her hands.

THE CASTLE

HESITANTLY, SHE CROSSED THE COURTYARD. Her burdens were lighter, and she surprisingly felt hope as she reached the massive golden door of the castle. She was still frightened, and she might have turned back, except for the presence of an old guard. He did not speak as she approached, though she sensed his kindness. The traveler's eyes were glued to the guard's boots, but she felt him gently pat her pack and rub her shoulder before he threw open the castle door. He then bent so she could see his hand pointing down a hallway to the right of the entry chamber. She was too surprised and too tired to question. She simply dragged her weary feet over the threshold and in the direction he had indicated.

The hallway was long, and at the end of it, the traveler wondered if she should turn around. When she stopped and looked back, the guard's black boots were gone and the entry door was closed.

The castle was growing darker. The sun had set outside its windows. Night was falling again, and her grumbling stomach reminded her that she'd had nothing to eat or drink all day. What should she do? She was too afraid to call out or knock on the single door in the hall. And if someone did happen to answer a knock, she wouldn't be able to enter anyway. Her pack was too big, even for the rooms of a king. Her shoulders slumped and began to heave as she slid down a brocade curtain and started to sob on the floor of the palace.

Without warning, someone was beside her. "Welcome," a man's voice said quietly. "Others would have given up long ago with burdens such as yours, but you are here. If only you could see the distance you have traveled. Know this: your journey was not without purpose. You shall see." The stranger placed a golden book in her lap and a plate of food beside her.

The traveler wiped her eyes and carefully opened the book's ancient cover. The pages seemed to glow with an inner light that filled the dimly lit hallway and illuminated the verses as she read.

As she feasted on the food and the words of the golden book, the man silently lifted boxes and burdens from the pack and whisked them away into the darkened hall behind her: Weakness, Fear, Loneliness, Shame.

Finally, the man removed the pack itself and shook it, sending rocks and pebbles skittering across the marble and littering the Persian rugs. The largest rock landed with a heavy thud next to the traveler, the crash breaking the marvelous spell of the book.

Startled, the traveler looked up and saw the huge stone trapping the fabric of her dress. Its label was dirty and smudged but still legible: *It Is My Fault. I Am to Blame.* This burden had been in her pack for a very long time.

The traveler wanted to hide. She was so ashamed that her secret was exposed for everyone to see. She struggled to push the rock off her dress so she could escape, but she was too embarrassed and too weary to make it budge. She was trapped in her humiliation. Tears formed in the traveler's eyes, and then she saw the man's feet through her tears.

"Oh, please, sir, can you lift this stone?"

Without a word, the man picked up the rock and hid it in the folds of his robe.

When the stone was gone, he reached down to take her hand. For the first time in many years, she was able to rise to her feet without tremendous effort. The only thing she carried was the book. The pack was gone. Yet, after being bent for so long, she couldn't straighten her body or raise her eyes to see the man at her side. With her gaze toward the floor, she followed the man into a room with a single staircase covered in a red carpet embroidered with gold and white doves.

THE THRONE

THE TRAVELER FROZE AS SHE realized she must be standing before the king's throne. She picked up her skirts and tried to curtsy. Her bent body, used to compensating for a heavy pack, tripped onto the stairs.

Her escort knelt at her side immediately. "Alas," he said, "I sense you haven't surrendered it all." And he gently lifted her chin with his hands.

As her eyes met his, the woman gasped, and she buried her face in her skirts again. The man kneeling before her, the man who had served her in the hall, was the king. On his head sat a golden crown, and a robe of deep-red velvet fell from his shoulders.

"My Lord," she whispered, "I beg your pardon. I did not know."

"Now you see clearly," the king said gently, lifting her chin again to peer intently into her eyes. "And yet, is there not one final burden you can give me?"

The traveler pondered the question, then reached around her neck and lifted a simple chain. At the end of the chain, sharp fragments of broken metal were all that was left of the figure of a heart. Somewhere along the road, the other piece of the broken pendant lay buried in the dirt.

The king took the broken heart and held it in the palm of his hand. Then he looked at the traveler for a long time before he said, "I have known the weight of your burdens. I have felt your sorrow and pain. Allow me to take the blame." With his other hand, he wiped away the last of the traveler's tears. Then he stood and lifted her to stand beside him. "There now," he said firmly. "Come with me. I have some gifts for you."

THE TREASURY

THE KING LED HER TO the treasury, which contained a large chest. Before he opened the lid, he turned to the traveler. "I honor you for your journey. I praise you for staying with us. I celebrate you for never giving up." He turned and brought out the first gift. It was a beautiful robe, hand-stitched in elaborate detail.

As she looked closer, the traveler saw scenes from her life, happy times in the past that she had somehow forgotten. Still other scenes pictured on the robe were strange and new. As she stared at the fabric, she wondered if the joyful images she did not recognize could be her future.

The king gently squeezed her shoulders after he draped the royal gift around her. Then he took the book she had been carrying and placed it in a pocket of the robe.

The king turned to the trunk again and brought out a jeweled box. As he opened it, the traveler saw a necklace. It was a heart pendant, like her own, the way

her necklace had looked in the beginning, but this one was much more beautiful. The metal gleamed with a rich shine, as if to say, "I am whole." As the king slipped the necklace around her neck, the traveler reached up to clasp the new heart in her hands.

The king then reached into the trunk one last time. He presented his third gift to the traveler on one knee. It was a beautiful crown embellished with diamonds and pearls.

Stunned, the traveler fell to her knees beside him, bowing her head to the ground. "Your majesty, you shouldn't. I'm not worthy of it."

The king did not stand but gently placed the crown
on her bowed head. "You are wrong," he told her.
"Your journey has caused you to forget who you are
and, more importantly, who I am. There is nothing I

have not done—indeed, there is nothing I would not do—for you. Let my actions express how precious you are to me."

As his words fell over her, the traveler straightened her shoulders and lifted her head. *He thinks I am beautiful*, she thought to herself. *The king loves me*. As her mind said these words, her heart confirmed them. The words were true, perhaps the truest in the world.

And there on his knees, the king pulled her close for a tender hug.

"Oh, thank you, thank you, my Lord," she whispered as she buried her face in his lap like a child.

The king stroked her hair and let her cry.

THE ROAD AGAIN

IN TIME, THE TRAVELER DRIED her eyes, took a deep breath, and stood to go. The king stood as well and watched her walk gracefully to the door. With her hand on the knob, the traveler stopped. She hesitated for a moment, then turned around and asked in a trembling voice, "Oh, Lord, must I leave you?"

The king's face beamed as he answered, "Whatever for?"

And so it was that on most days, the king and the traveler journeyed together. Often she went searching for those who were burdened as she had been so she could bring them back to the king. Some nights she thought about the strangers who had helped her, and she wondered if she would ever meet them again. She wanted to thank them for guiding her to this path, a path so different from the one she had traveled before. She was grateful for her ability to carry heavy loads now because she carried a new pack, this one filled with food and clothing, books and blankets, and pretty scarves for those in need. These gifts were wonderful, but the new pack did not hold her greatest offering. There was something else the traveler carried that friends and strangers needed even more. Her greatest gift was the hope that shone like bright candles in her eyes.

POSTSCRIPT BY
THE AUTHOR

I BEGAN THIS STORY AFTER struggling for many months with severe depression. I wanted to share my testimony of Christ's power to heal us. I know this healing doesn't always happen immediately. Sometimes He asks us to keep carrying our burdens while He strengthens us. He makes it possible for us to shoulder our loads. I know I have needed my trials to make me stronger and more like Him. I have learned for myself that the Atonement's power provides comfort, assurance, and relief on the road.

I hope this simple parable will open the door for a discussion about mental health challenges. My desire was not to simplify or minimize the pain of those who struggle but to provide encouragement and prompt inspiration through the Holy Ghost. To learn more about how to share these ideas, see thetravelerandtheheavyburden.blogspot.com.

So many of us want to be like the innkeeper, the older woman at the gate, the younger woman in the market, and the castle guard, but we don't know how. If someone you love is feeling hopeless, help them feel hope. Help them know that things will get better. They will not always feel this way. If they are feeling helpless, lead them to the help they need. Support them in searching for solutions until things improve. If they are feeling worthless, affirm their eternal worth as a son or daughter of God. They are needed. Life is not better without them. They are loved.

Finally, for those who are struggling with depression or other mental health challenges, I say to you, "It is not your fault. You are not to blame." This was the message I felt the Holy Ghost wanted me to convey through the king. I know the Savior loves you and has great things in store for your life. Trust Him. Lean on Him. He is mighty to save.

ABOUT THE AUTHOR

Deborah Pace Rowley spent six months as a college student living in England and exploring the world of her favorite authors, including Dickens, Wordsworth, Jane Austen, and the Brownings. She has never recovered from the writing and travel bugs she contracted those many years ago. She loves visiting historical sites with her family and sharing her passion for words with her students. Deborah hopes that in some small way, she can help others and leave a lasting legacy with her own inspiring stories.

ABOUT THE
ILLUSTRATOR

Sarah D. Newell is an illustrator with a passion for well-woven stories.

"I have found that with something as simple as a piece of paper and a pencil, a person can touch hearts and bring light into people's lives. That is exactly what this beautiful story has done for me. We all go through trials in our lives, but if we are able to lift our heads, we will see countless helpers along the way, eager to lighten our load."

Sarah never leaves the house without her sketchbook and, at any given moment, can be found enjoying the local wildflowers with her family. She and her husband live at the foothills of the Rockies and share their home with their corgi Marvel and a rabbit named Dandelion.